HARD SELL

PUNCH Among the Commercials

Edited by William Hewison

A PUNCH BOOK
Published in association with
GRAFTON BOOKS
A Division of the Collins Publishing Group

LONDON GLASGOW
TORONTO SYDNEY AUCKLAND

Grafton Books
A Division of the Collins Publishing Group
8 Grafton Street, London W1X 3LA

Published by Grafton Books 1989

British Library Cataloguing in Publication Data

Hard sell: Punch among the commercials.
1. English humorous cartoons – Collections
I. Hewison, William II. Punch
741.5'942

ISBN 0-246-13579-4

Printed in Great Britain by
William Collins Sons Ltd, Glasgow

Introduction

Remember him, the chap who rings your bell and announces that he is doing some special research in your district and it would be a great help if you could answer just a few questions, won't take more than five minutes, what a pleasant little crescent this is, so leafy and yet so close to the centre of town?

Flattered (and gullible), you invite him in out of the rain and prepare to dole out your invaluable opinions on whatever it is he wants to know. Half-way into his five minutes the light begins to glimmer through and you realise that before much longer what he's going to do is try and sign you up for a set of expensive encyclopaedias.

Is this character part of a vanishing species, along with the 'students' pushing magazine subscriptions and the man itching to demonstrate the latest thing in vacuum cleaners? What we get nowadays is the telephone call in the middle of supper from the double-glaziers and the life-insurance pedlars; the foot in the door has been replaced by a sales-pitch via Telecom.

Which is bad news for the toiling cartoonist; after all, in the past he has stacked up an impressive pile of gags based on the activities of these door-to-door hucksters and is loath to lose that part of his meal ticket. Over a period of time these wage-door Johnnies appeared so regularly in the public prints they became firmly implanted as a cartoon cliché; nevertheless, top-ranking cartoonists like Leslie Starke persisted in producing fresh and sublime examples of the genre, so who's grumbling? One such, by Starke, is deeply notched in the memory: a perky encyclopaedia salesman confronts a low-browed pug-ugly on the doorstep. He begins his spiel: 'You get into an argument, say, about the Gnostic Heresy, or the influence of Palladio on English architecture...'

But the art of prising people from their money by gentle (as well as rigorous) persuasion is a task which goes far beyond that doorstep brigade, and the *Punch* comic artists whose inventions appear in the following pages demonstrate that they are up to most of the tricks, covering as they do a comprehensive spectrum of humour and using a great diversity of drawing styles: TV commercials, book promotions, the activities of the advertising agencies and the Public Relations mafiosi, with special attention to the extravagances of second-hand car salesmen and wily estate agents; also the selling techniques of the large department stores as well as the tiny boutiques of the *Just Sox* variety – they all get the treatment. The spread is wide enough to include the vanishing sandwich-board man touting alongside the sportsman covered in a patchwork of company logos; sales, salesgirls, sharp practices, the beckoning of special offers – they all come in for comic scrutiny.

And quite right too, because selling and advertising is nothing much more than Promises, Promises – and the buyer certainly needs to beware. Hence this warning: if a character dressed up as a jesting buffoon knocks on your door and tells you he is Kartoony Ken and offers you £10 if you can produce a copy of this book – don't let him in.

William Hewison
March 1989

"The first time was bad enough – the book-promotion is killing me."

"Well, yes, I have just written my autobiography – it's called 'Bed Girl', published by Ace Books at two pounds sixty and I shall be signing copies tomorrow in the book department at – oops! I nearly advertised."

"I understand you've written a book on how to get free plugs on television."

"It's a matter of principle, really, but I have to believe in a product before I'm prepared to tell lies about it."

VEGE
FRUIT
SPECIAL
AS SEEN AT THE TATE GALLERY
Brillo

CHECKOUT

"Love it!"

"Listen, mate, you think I enjoy being lumbered with the tequila promotion?"

"Okay, so we don't attack at night, but that doesn't mean we can't earn a living."

"See here, Ritterhaus, I want TV commercials that will give people headaches and upset-stomachs."

"Don't look now, but behind you I think life is beginning to imitate television commercials."

"Taxi!"

"Bleedin' Trades Description Act!"

"Sanctuary! I'm escaping advertising."

"Aye, it were a bad day for pigeon racing when t'advertising boys got into it."

"What the hell do we want with double-glazing?"

"I got them from the same guy that sells us the rifles and fire-water."

"Is it true you're a famous racing driver?"

"Do you think he'll be annoyed when he notices we've sold the soft drinks concession?"

FORD
PEPSI
COLA
MARTELL
CAMEL
SONY
CARLSBERG
HARRODS
NIKE

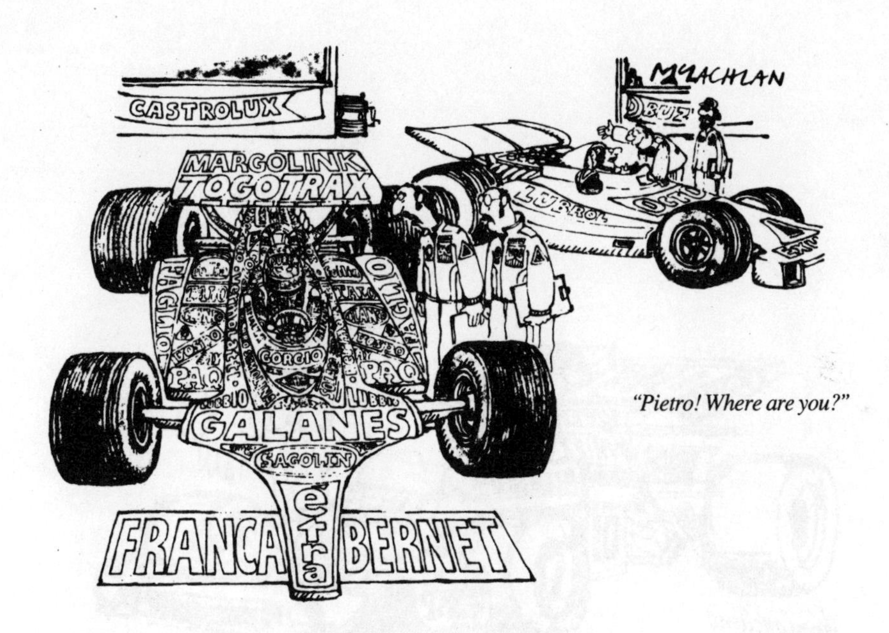

"Pietro! Where are you?"

"Of course, it's only really held together by the lettering."

"Hey – this one's dented and scratched!"

"Let's see what we can do for you, sir – 30p to knock out the dent, 25p for a respray, 40p labour charge . . ."

"We find the price is one of the most important safety features
...it makes one drive very slowly."

"I don't like the look of it. Shoddy workmanship . . . type out of alignment . . . colours not in key . . . literals galore . . . staples all rusting . . ."

"...and, as you can see, it's right bang in the Martini belt."

COUNTRY COTTAGE
FOR SALE
LONDON ONLY
6 MILES AWAY
5 4 3 2
Ken Pyne

"Here you are, squire – genuine fifteenth-century, all mod cons, etc. Course, you haven't got a hope in hell of getting a mortgage."

"It looks as though the 1st Battalion, Estate Agents' Volunteer Rifles are going to be the last to retreat again!"

"It'll be a heavenly place for us to retire to – whenever my wife gets stroppy!"

"We've decided to put it on the market."

"There's 5000 acres of arable, with Elizabethan farmhouse and cottages, but it's well below your price range."

"It's not really for sale – we just don't see many people out here."

"Do let's buy it, Geoffrey."

"It is reputed to be one of the finest and largest in England – one hundred and thirty feet high, with a capacity of eight million cubic feet. Dating from nineteen hundred and ten, it took two years to build. Over ninety thousand rivets, it's…"

"What's your first reaction?"

"Let us pause awhile and drink in that breathtaking view."

"...And here we have the fully-fitted kitchen."

DOWN
3P
6P
OFF
NOW WITH
IMPROVED
SURVEILLANCE
CAMERAS!
Hawker

"So it's powerful. I still don't want one."

"The name escapes me but it was advertised on television and it adds a certain piquancy to even the humblest stew."

AUTO
ACCESSORIES
AUTO
ACCESSORIES
SPECIAL
OFFER
RADIATOR
SEALANT
½ PRICE
NOEL
FORD

"Give it a wheel round and see how it feels!"

"I wanted something for a rather more feminine type of man."

"Would it be all right to dilute it with water to begin with?"

SIGGS

"Which do you recommend – the one with the high running costs, the brand that is electrically unsafe and difficult to service, or the one with the poor finish and unreliable thermostat?"

"Of course, you can get it ten pence cheaper at the supermarket, but what can you get for ten pence these days?"

"We only stock those products that haven't been tested on live animals, don't exploit the Third World, and of which the advertising doesn't degrade women, men, children, or the dignity of the class struggle."

"Shoppe!"

ANTIQUES
NEW YORK TIMES

"I'll be damned – someone's slipped us a counterfeit fiver."

"I'm not asking you to serve me – just to include me in your conversation."

"I'll have the avocado shampoo accompanied by the egg conditioner, with the oyster and cider vinegar cleansing milk to follow, and perhaps just a tiny pot of peach and strawberry hand cream to finish off with…"

"I'm sorry, sir, we're out of Portly but we can do you a nice Stout."

"You'll have heard about our new sales policy – if you don't want the encyclopaedias all you have to do is say 'No'."

"I'd like a hard sell if you could manage one."

"Will you be paying by cheque, credit card, money, or are you shoplifting?"

"Actually, no. 'Congratulations on Having Your Murder Charge Reduced to Manslaughter' doesn't sell very well."

"It's my first epidemic."

MOTHERS DAY CARDS
FATHERS DAY
GREAT AUNTS DAY
RAND DADS DAY
NEW!
GREETINGS CARD MANUFACTURERS DAY

"Lot 7. Vermicelli's 'Temptation of the Art Dealers'."

"Ah, but are you unknown ***enough****?"*

"All that stuff pays the rent, of course, but I keep the important things over here."

"Business is terrible. Nobody wants the big stuff any more."

"Don't worry about not making a sale, young man – I can show you how to slash your heating bills by up to 25 per cent."

"You get into an argument, say, about the Gnostic Heresy, or the influence of Palladio on English architecture ..."

"I'm afraid you have a wrong number, sir, however, sir ..."

"Oh, just some salesman trying to sell karate books."

"I see the Jehovah's Witnesses have developed a new marketing strategy."

"Good morning, madam. We are Jehovah's Witnesses, Double-Glazing division…"

"I have reason to believe that you are pushing dope."

'THE JERICHO MAIL'
GOOD SAMARITAN
WILL BE IN THIS AREA
TODAY
CORRECTLY IDENTIFY
HIM AND WIN
FREE ACCOMMODATION
IN THE INN OF YOUR
CHOICE

"Good afternoon – my company is conducting a survey in this area…"

"Guess what, Mum – Arnie's Salesman of the Month again."

FAST SNAX
OPEN
KWIK KLEEN
2 HOUR DRY KLEEN
SECKS SHOP
ADULT VIDEOS, BOOKS, MAGS

"Don't take any notice if people laugh at you – they laughed at Beethoven."

"Our suspicions were correct! He is selling information to the other side."

"For the last time, I don't want any lavender!"

Simply SOCKS
Mere Bagatelles

EATS
APPLE PIE
JUST LIKE THE BIRD
WHO SHACKED
WITH YOUR OLD
MAN USED TO
MAKE
15p
HEATH

"Well, we do make a small charge for agreeing not to gazump the price."

"I'm all for truth in advertising, but I really must draw the line at 'Smith and Bastard'..."

"I like it. It's a nice blend of truth, half-truth and anything but the truth."

"All right, let's hear ***your*** *idea of how a trapped food particle would sound shouting for help as the dentifrice penetrates!"*

"The makers of Sno-Glo want to wish you warm season's greetings and happiness in the New Year. The cost of this fifteen-second spot announcement is hidden in the purchase price of your next box of Sno-Glo. Thank you and God bless you."

"For sale. Twenty thousand German helmets never been used. Ideal for parties, house plants or motor-cycle gangs."

"This is treachery – they've stolen our deceptive wording that gets round the Trades Description Act."

SAILS
HUNNY-SWETE FOODS
LITE® DESSERTS
Kool® ICE CREAM
KRUNCH®CEREAL
Nick

"Mum!"

"When commercials like this drive you to drink, try one of these."

DON'T MISS OUR
FANTASTIC
NEW SEASON
OF EXCITING
SERVICES
FROM THE PEOPLE
WHO GAVE YOU
CHRISTMAS!

"In addition to the street entertainment offence, you are also charged with contravention of the Trades Description Act."

"You need have no fear of that book. The bare bum on the cover does not occur anywhere in the story."

"The legendary curse also applies to those who don't buy a souvenir."

"I'll just bet they look nothing like that when we actually get the brochures."

"We came here to get away from all those holiday ads on television."

"Another thing about Liechtenstein – their road maps are really easy to fold."

"Of course, I've had to diversify a bit since the crowds fell off."

"Maybe you'd like something to drink, sir, before the mirage starts."

"Business is terrible."

"Here we have our economy line, sir."

CASHIER
71
HONEYSETT

"Bad news, Partridge – the computers can sell themselves now."

"Side effects? I promise not to call again for at least six months."

"Well, they are very good quality matches."

"Congratulations! You have been chosen out of two million people to have me certified!"

"Good afternoon. I'm a confidence trickster and I've come to swindle you out of your life savings…"

"There's another rep to see you."

INVENTED THE SWISS ARMY KNIFE, BUT FORGOT TO PATENT IT.
SCHWADRON

BUSINESS STINKS SALE
30% OFF ALL ITEMS

"Let's get moving. I'm beginning to feel like an advert for a pension fund."

"I understand it's such a success they're planning to close down from larger premises."

THE SWAN
BAR
JUKE BOX
POP GROUP
TOPLESS BARMAIDS!
FRUIT MACHINES
DISCO
STRIPTEASE
THE GEORGE
ALES
NO TOPLESS BARMAIDS
NO POP GROUP
NO JUKE BOX
NO STRIPTEASE
NO FRUIT MACHINES
NO DISCO
PUBLIC BAR
KenPyne

"It's got more special-function keys than you'll find on many of the larger models: square root, cosine, logarithmic, integral and exponential keys. I'd say that more than makes up for the fact that it doesn't have the number nine!"

"Decision time. Do we want 'The Original', 'Award-Winning' or 'New and Improved'?"

"This one frankly admits it's overpriced."

K. SMITH OPTICIAN 68
Baxter

FE'S BARGAIN BAZAAR
WAY OUT
YOU ARE WELCOME TO WALK ROUND

"This, of course, is the basic standard model."

"You'll be surprised when you see the low mileage she's done."

"The gardener's off sick."

"I feel the only question Sir has to ask himself is if Sir is prepared for the amount of crumpet Sir will attract."

"He wants to look under the bonnet!"

"But remember, by the time it's paid for you'll be that much older and more mature – less keen on speed, flashy appearance, cutting a dash."

special this week
manhattan island,
very cheap

"But why spend good money on a surveyor's report? I can tell you what it would say – rising damp, dry rot, unsafe wiring – you know their jargon."

"I should decide quickly. It may be gone by tomorrow."

"Ah, I see that Sir has hidden depths."

"And then there was this other bit of irresistible temptation in the spring sales, Father…"

"...And now a nice big hand for Mrs Forsyth for kindly providing us with a typical family wash."

"They're detached of course."

"Genuine Polar rock, guv . . . every stick has 'Great God! This is an awful place' written all the way through . . ."

"Dora, what does Market Research say about our new line?"

"Market Research reports that 'Painted Lady' is going like a bomb round the docks."

"If it's any consolation – it was instantaneous."

"I want a good clean fight with nothing that would adversely affect the sales of your sponsor's products."

"By Jove! A customer!"

"What do you think
– is it me?"

"Look at 'em, undignified bunch of amateurs. Placards moving too fast to be read. All this shouting – not content with the power of the printed word. First windy corner and they'll be struggling! Won't have the know-how to lean ***into*** *the wind…"*

"Sorry I'm late – I got lost."

"Notice the rickety staircase, the uneven sloping floors, the walls out of alignment . . ."

"Attractive, unattached mid-lifer seeking adventure and companionship meet fun-loving, mature single wishing to share travel and togetherness."

"As I see it, gentlemen, our next step is to find a market for Design No. 2."

SELL US YOUR CAR
WE BUY YOUR CAR FOR CASH!!!
HIGHEST PRICES OFFERED
BRING YOUR CAR TO US.
WE ARE EAGER BUYERS

"Yes?"

"If it's only another book club offer, why are you eating it?"